Susan Alexis & Br

Happy adventures!
♡
Sus y

FROM A TO ZEN

Illustrations by: Natalia Pirogova

Dear Reader,

From A to Zen is a complete follow along yoga flow for children. You are about to embark on a fantastic yoga adventure! This interactive story is designed to help children (and adults) flow through various poses while practicing mindful movements. Each letter of the alphabet has its own yoga tale to tell and naturally transitions into the next pose.

All you have to do is carefully follow the directions and illustrations on each page. Use your imagination, find your voice, get into character, and have fun!

Your authors,
Susan & Brett

From A to Zen – An ABC Yoga Adventure
Copyright 2021
Author: Susan Alexis and Brett Drew
Illustrator: Natalia Pirogova
Editor: Melanie Lopata & Bobbie Hinman
All rights reserved.
No part of this publication may be reproduced, stored in a retrieval system, or transmitted in any form or by any means, electronic, mechanical, photocopying, recording or otherwise, with the prior permission of the copyright owner.
ISBN 9780578999579
MADD Liebs LLC

ARCHER

Graceful and strong, the archer springs to her feet,
plucking an arrow from her quiver,
then knocks it to her bow.
She draws back as far as she can reach,
and is now ready to launch.

She is careful to avoid the...

BOPPING BULLFROG

Jolly and adorable, the bullfrog playfully smiles.
As he bends his knees all the way down,
he sits on his heels with his hands and feet upon
his throne.
Then he winds up, ready to take a giant leap into
the air.

He leaps all the way up to the…

CLOUD CASTLE

Airy and light, the arms, like twin towers,
stretch high and bright,
rising on toes with a gently arched back,
feeling a great, powerful full body stretch.

Then comes a gust of wind from the incredible...

DYNAMIC DRAGON

Mighty and stout, the dragon kneels low
while keeping his chin high.
His chest rises as he takes a deep breath in
through his snout,
then holds it for 3...2...1...

Until he blows it directly towards the...

ENCHANTED ELVIN WARRIOR

Brave and lithe, the warrior lunges deeply
and raises his hands together,
palms facing forward, shielding himself from danger.

Yet, all around him flit the...

FOREST FAIRY FLOWERS

Nimble and quick, the fairy flowers feel the golden rays of sunshine.
With knees together and slightly bent, they tuck in their elbows
and point their fingers skyward.

They fling themselves at the...

GLITTERING GRYPHON

Shiny and bright, the gryphon sits back on his haunches.
Reaching out, he catches the flowers in mid-air.

He is ready to pounce on the...

HEROIC HERON

Fearless and calm, the heron lowers her knees
to the ground,
resting the tops of her feet on the floor.
With toes pointed back, she lifts her heart
with great pride
and places her palms upon her lap,
embracing the fresh air and the brisk wind.

She descends towards the...

INCREDIBLE ILLUSIONIST

Mystical and limber, the illusionist rises slowly,
with knees slightly bent.
Intertwining his arms,
he then lifts one leg over the other.

He unwinds as he reaches for his...

JITTERY JAR OF JITTERS

Excited and passionate, the jittery jar

Jit-Jit jits his fingers,

Touch-Touch touches her shoulders,

Tap-Tap taps his toes,

Twist-Twist twists her hips.

Until they calmly approach the...

KINDRED KALEIDOSCOPE

Fascinating and brilliant, the kaleidoscope of color,
with a spectrum of shapes, forms graceful crescents,
shining her light.
With arms over her head, her body
slowly bends towards the side.

She gazes wistfully at the glow cast by the....

LUMINOUS LANTERNS

Dazzling and bright, the lantern jumps with
her feet and arms apart,
turning one foot out and dipping her body to that side.
Setting one arm upon her shin,
she watches as she releases a floating globe with the
other arm.

She gazes at the glowing light rising playfully towards the...

MAJESTIC MOONDANCER

Radiant and soft, the moondancer takes a step forward
and leaves that foot gently upon the surface of the moon.
She slowly kicks her other foot behind her as high as it
can go.
Reaching back with one hand to grasp her toes,
she extends the other arm up high.

Mindfully, she holds her balance,
while under the watchful eyes of the...

NIGHT NINJA

Stealthy and silent, the ninja lowers
his leg into a deep ninja lunge.
One arm extends firmly back as the
other extends forward,
creating a perfectly straight line,
his shadow energy builds up in his
front fingertips.

He beams the energy at the…

ORNERY OGRE

Slow but strong, the ogre twists away
from the powerful beam,
placing his elbow by the outside of his
front knee.
Hands together, he absorbs the blast
with his powerful shoulder.

He looks out towards the...

PIRATE PIXIE

Spritely and spry, the pixie faces forward towards the sea.
She nimbly lowers the side of her front leg to the ground,
while fully extending the other leg back behind her.
Her torso sits tall, her arms down beside her.

She is carefree and unaware of the presence of the....

QUESTING QUEEN

Regal in disguise, the queen slides her front leg back
to meet the other.
She lies flat on her stomach to avoid detection,
lifting her binoculars to her eyes
and resting her elbows on the ground.

She is in search of the magical fairy dust that will
fly her up to the...

RADIANT RAINBOW

Divine and creative, she rolls onto her back,
hands placed down on the ground.
Her feet plant firmly on the rainbow gleam,
and she pushes her body off the ground.
Extending her hips skyward,
she creates a rainbow of her own.

The rainbow dew splashes upon the...

SWINGING SPRITE

Delicate and dainty, the sprite lowers herself to sit
upon her swing.
She leans back and reaches her arms out.
Gliding through the sky,
she lifts her perfectly straight legs all the way out in
the air.

Her forward momentum propels her towards the...

TRANQUIL TROLL

Steady and tall, the troll moves her great bulk
towards the sky,
lifting the massive weight of one powerful foot.
While bending her knee outward,
she rests her foot just above her other knee
and extends her arms out like the branches of a tree.

She gazes in wonder at the distant...

UNICORN

Noble and wondrous, the unicorn lowers her hooves
down to the ground, shoulder-width apart.
She steps back with both feet,
then lifts her hips up in the air
and feels a deep stretch along her back and calves.

She is unwilling to be captured by the...

VALIANT VIKING

Raw and untamed, the viking lowers his hips
until his back is perfectly straight,
arms fully extended, tightening his core.
His toes are firmly planted as he gazes directly ahead.

Suddenly, he observes the...

WHIRLING WIZARD

Rambunctious and spellbound,
the wizard pivots perpendicular to his giant scroll
and lies flat.
Hearing danger, he casts a Chameleon spell,
grabs the edges of his scroll,
and rolls himself up like a log.

Breathlessly, he waits as he hides from the...

XANTHIUS

Jovial and sly, he rolls along the riverbank,
his webbed toes splashing softly in the river.
Coming to a stop, he faces the sky
and rests his palms along his sides.
He lifts his back off the ground,
while letting his head fall backwards,
chin pointing to the sky.

Looking behind him, he spots the...

YAWNING YOGI

Mindful and poised, the yogi shifts herself to a
seated position,
crossing her legs with knees upon the ground.
Her hands rest delicately on her knees.
Her eyes gently close as she takes a breath of
fresh air.

She is getting ready to rest for a moment of...

ZEN

Peaceful and still, lying softly on her back,
her arms and legs outstretched,
she breathes slowly in and out through her nose.
Quieting her mind, she feels the stillness
and the energy radiating from her chest,

down through her fingertips
and all the way to her toes.
She quietly appreciates the
enchanting moment of peace.

Namaste.

ARCHER

FOREST FAIRY FLOWER

BOPPING-BULLFROG

GLITTERING GRYPHON

CLOUD CASTLE

DYNAMIC DRAGON

HEROIC HERON

INCREDIBLE ILLUSIONIST

ENCHANTED ELVIN WARRIOR

JITTERY JAR OF JITTERS